1 Walked out of 2 and Forgot It

by Toby MacLennan

1972
Something Else Press, Inc.
Millerton   Barton   Berlin

ISBN 0–87110–083–5 (hardbound edition)
ISBN 0–87110–084–3 (paper edition)
L. C. Catalog Card No: 75–189887

MANUFACTURED IN THE UNITED STATES OF AMERICA.

1 Walked Out of 2 and Forgot It

The sky was using a tree to dig a hole in the earth.

For the past couple of days he had been having terrible pains in his left eye and decided to see someone about it. The doctor decided surgery was necessary, and rushing him to the hospital, immediately removed from his eye the tree, the house, the rock and the ball.

As she passed him on the street he thought he recognized her and looked at her intently. She in turn felt his glance and turned to look at him. They realized they had never seen each other before and continued on their way, she to his house and he to hers.

A violent tornado spiraled into a small stream and damaged its memory.

He stood at the table wrapping a package he intended to send to someone through the mail. With one hand he wrapped the package and with the other hand he unwrapped it.

As he left the room to go to the post office, he came into the room with the package.

He unwrapped the package and was delighted, as was his friend who received it through the mail.

At times he was in the habit of pacing back and forth in his room. One morning when he turned around, he found it impossible to take a step, as the room had filled up with his walking.

When the baby was born there was no one to tell it whether it was a stone or a cup.

He could not conceive of living in the center of an infinitely empty eggshell. Everywhere he looks, he sees something. And one thing leads only to another.

It is as if he had intentionally wallpapered on his existence. A black sheet with white dots had been rolled onto the boundaries of space and something called a bottom had been laid down beneath him. Shapes of spaces were then hammered in, between which were glued three-dimensional pictures of houses and rooms and tables and chairs and streets and cities. He filled all the spaces and took a position within the picture.

One morning, having nothing to get up for, he remained in bed for some time. He looked at his arm lying on the sheet of the bed and then to the space between his bed and the small table next to him. His eyes moved slowly over the table into a more arbitrary space between that object and a straight backed chair. He followed the chair to the bureau drawers which held a large mirror that saw everything he saw, but all at once. And then the large space next to the bureau which could be re-arranged according to the position of the door. And the door itself, closed, a doorknob holding a shirt. The door blocked his vision, he had no choice but to go back to himself through the spaces he had come. The doorknob holding a shirt. A bureau, a mirror, a chair, a space, the table and another space, his bed under the sheets upon which he had laid his arm. Everywhere things cascaded into his vision and filled it.

He sat up on the edge of the bed and yawned. He walked over to the door and took his shirt from the knob. He slipped one of his arms into the shirt and reached for the other sleeve. Somehow he couldn't slip this side over his shoulder and turned his head to see what the trouble was. As he looked to his side, he could see quite clearly that like a piece of paper whose edge has begun to curl, a cor-ner of his shoulder was peeling away from itself, uncovering a large piece of white space.

He was sitting in a field thinking that the inside of his body was filling up with water at exactly the same moment that he drowned.

He knew that when the mirror came it would bring with it all the articles he wanted to be seen with today.

In his room there was a bed, a closet, a table, a chair and a telephone with his number on it. There was a door on the far end of the room.

One morning he got up from his bed and walked to the door at the end of the room. He opened it and walked into a room exactly like his own, the same crumpled sheets on the bed, a closet with his clothes hanging in it, a table, a chair and a telephone with his number on it. There was a door on the far end of the room. He walked to the door, opened it and stepped into his original room.

The continual leaving of his molecules in the form of a picture image had left him exhausted. He therefore decided against appearance and was never seen again, although he continued the rest of his daily life as usual.

He called out . . . doorknob . . . rhinoceros . . . cup . . . glass . . . stone, but each word simply fell on top of the one before it.

It is impossible to tell what makes him move. There is no apparent cord or other connection, yet he is able to be in one position at one moment and suddenly in another position in the next.

He was standing in a room behind a door. He turned the handle of the panel, opened it and stepped through the hole into another room. He took a step to cross the room. He took another step, and one more, then again, until he arrived across the floor in front of a door.

Although he has been seen going through this procedure many times, and each time it is obvious that he appears in many positions within this room, he repeatedly only allows himself to be seen in one of these positions at a time.

He was standing in an area from which he could be watched. He started out very carefully to cross a street. As he got to the other side, he stopped at the curb for some seconds, apparently looking down at something. Then he quickly stepped up onto the sidewalk, hurried to the nearest shop and stopped in front of it.

While he stood in front of the building, I looked into the street to see him pausing at the curb, but he was gone.

There was a bed, a stone in the middle of the floor and a door on the far side of it. As he could remember a thing for only 3 seconds, in the morning he would leave the bed but by nightfall he was still on this side of the rock.

On the table sat a grapefruit made out of a hole.

Many years ago he had lived alone in a small room much like his present one, and had a job in a shop. But he had forgotten all this.

This morning when he woke up, the curtain drifting slightly in front of the open window reminded him of something he wasn't quite sure of, but as he couldn't remember what it was, he got up and walked to the shop.

He took the shape of a bowl in order to eat out of it.

He heard the sound come over the hill but before it reached him, it vanished. He smelled the grass coming over the hill, but before it got to him, the smell was gone. He saw the man come over the hill but before it could reach him, his image ran out.

He had a choice of being the wave that rolls onto the shore or the one that rolls into the sea.

. He was waiting at a curb for the traffic light to change when something he vaguely recognized crossed in front of him. When the green light flashed, he hurried to catch up, and drawing up behind, made an effort to call its attention. He reached out to make contact and suddenly felt his hand slipping over the back of the day.

Both of them closed their eyes at the same time, thus neither was able to see the other. When he opened his eyes, they still were unable to see each other, as he had also opened his.

Ten deceased people stood in a museum case displaying an everyday scene of a funeral parlor.

That night he was visiting a friend and they were talking. He began to tell his companion of the strange thing he had seen today. As he was walking in the country he stopped to look around. He saw a man standing at some distance, but directly across from him. The man was standing in an empty space, somewhat behind but between a large tree and a smaller hill. The strange thing was that together with these two objects, a perfect triangle was formed, with the man at the apex standing quite still looking at him.

One day during the next week, he went to a museum. Objects were all neatly arranged in glass cases and sat on special pieces of cloth. He was moving slowly from case to case when he noticed in one, a collection of rocks. Each of these rocks had been dusted and separated from the others. As he looked at each stone, he noticed that every one was just a little different from the next. When he came to the end of the case, his eye was caught by one particular rock. As he looked closer, he saw that embedded in the rock was a small but complete scene of a landscape.

Three people were sitting in a room talking of time and the inability to reverse it. One person gestured into the space of the room, demonstrating the impossibility of retracting something that has already been done and then brought his hand back to its original position.

He misplaced himself on the bus and when he reboarded the same coach, he was unable to recognize himself.

When he got home he realized he had left his feet under the table at the restaurant.

One windy day the smells from a large field blew to one corner and made a nose.

The man was walking with a bird. They came upon a crease in the paper. He bent down and ripped out a piece of the fold and turned it over in his hands. He looked at it and then put it down in the same place. The bird pecked at the paper until the piece fell through the hole. When the man looked through the hole and saw the paper hit the ground, he painted in the background flat gray.

Just as a plant might shoot up in one type of soil and in another ground might not sprout at all, he was growing quite well in a stone.

In the middle of his living room stood a frozen life size model of himself pouring a pitcher of water in a field when he was eight years old.

He was dressed in a suit and sitting at the back of a rowboat that was drifting on a motionless sea. For as far as he could see there was only a still gray sky and the large body of smooth water, except for a gray cube floating far out in the water which was a man sitting at the back of a motionless rowboat.

In order to save the boy from falling into the hole, he pushed him into it.

Four people sat around a table discussing what they were doing at the moment of doing it.

One said, "I am now holding my hand in the air."

Each raised his hand in the air and in his hand held a scale model of someone sitting alone in a room.

Each of the four was alone in his own house.

He stood in the chair while he crossed the floor and he picked up the square box as he looked out of the window, he moved the chair closer to him and sat down as he walked out of the empty room.

As he couldn't remember it and she had forgotten, they kept thinking about it.

He always appears with a thing. He has appeared with a doorknob, a tree, a chair, a sky, a door, a ground, a clock, a space, a yellow, a noise, a bouncing ball, a fly.

He also appears in a space at 2:15 beneath a tree, sitting in a chair with his shoes resting on the ground. A fly buzzes his ear as a yellow bouncing ball moves past him to bump up against a door.

Only once was he seen without anything else.

A cell isolated from his hand was forced to grow to the size of a marble. In it they found a picture of a fork.

He was bombarded by various memories. An A and an Of, the toe of a shoe, a half of an apple. That night as he sat down for dinner, a stone dripped out of his ear.

He boarded the bus, paid his fare and took a seat somewhere in the front. He looked around arbitrarily until his eyes fell on a woman across the way from him. She happened to look at him at the same time, and catching each other, they smiled politely.

His stop came up and he rang the buzzer. The bus pulled to a stop. He pushed the doors open and stepped down. Just as the bus was pulling away, he had a compulsion to reach up to his nose whereupon he suddenly realized that he had exchanged faces with the woman.

He existed as a perfect sphere and rolled from room to room.

He opened the door to a room at the far end of which a man stood looking out of a window.

As he stepped through the doorway, the other man fell through the glass.

He placed a large double sided mirror down the center of his body and both figures left the room.

He went to the refrigerator and took out a sandwich and a glass of milk. He sat down in a chair, picked up a magazine and looked through it as he ate the sandwich. He finished, went over to the bed and laid down for a nap. When he got up he went to the refrigerator and took out a sandwich and a glass of milk. He sat down in a chair and picking up the magazine, looked through it as he ate the sandwich.

The number 1 walked out of the number 2 and forgot it.

Standing in one corner of the building, he looked out of the window and saw an elm tree standing on the grass. He walked to the next corner of the building and looking out of the window, saw the elm tree. At the third corner he looked out seeing the tree and grass and walking to the forth corner he looked out of the window and saw the elm tree standing on the grass.

He cut time into symmetrical parts, keeping one of the halves for himself and giving the other to an anonymous lady carrying her groceries out of a supermarket.

As the lady had gotten amnesia, he came to live with her as her memory.

They had all come to the park for a picnic. One of the guests brought a large chunk of cheese which sat in the center of the table cloth. He became amused with the cheese and broke off a piece to hold in his hand. He sat staring at it for some time. Then he put the piece into his mouth and began to chew it. When he swallowed it, he was blind.

When he died, an unknown man came to the family and spent the rest of his life in the home, wearing a mask of the deceased.

Looking through the microscope, he took a small knife and divided the part into two. Then he took the smaller part and divided that into two. Soon he employed a more powerful lens and another until he needed a microscopic sized pin to divide the parts. When he touched the pin to the next particular part, it struck against it and scratched the surface.

He went out for a walk in order to consider this event when glancing up to the sky he suddenly saw that part of it had been ripped.

In the full light of day, the man walking down the street grew darker.

He was walking downtown. He had been thinking of an irregular shape.

A bus pulled up along side him and as the noise was suddenly jarring, he stopped in the middle of the sidewalk. His attention was immediately caught by the building in front of him and as he turned to look at it, he saw that two stories up his thought was hanging on the edge of a window ledge.

As it became necessary to use everything over and over, the aunt sat on the table in the shape of a teacup.

He stood in a room, a companion stood 10 feet from him. The first one attracted a small object to his hand. He turned and faced the other. This one put his hand in the air as did the first. Without warning, the object suddenly wrenched itself from the first hand, flew across the room and clung to the hand of the other.

The man had been frozen before death and thus when he slipped from the attendant's hands, he shattered into splinters on the floor.

There were five people standing in a circle. Each one faced the center and looked into it. The first member of the circle said he saw a man standing in the center whom he recognized as Jack. The second member said he saw Jack in the center. The third member also had no doubt that it was Jack and each of the last two said they saw Jack. The five people in the circle were all named Jack.

The motion of his walking from the chair to the door was used as the word 'and' in the sentence, 'He walked to the door.'

The girl was looking at all the pictures of herself before she died.

This afternoon he was walking down a busy street. He stopped now and then to look in a store window at one object or another. A certain object in one of the windows caught his eye and he stopped to browse inside the shop. After some moments he returned to the street, looked at the object once more through the window and continued walking.

Slightly but noticeably, he began to accelerate his pace. He began to walk a little faster. He then quickened this pace even more. Then faster. And faster. Soon he was hurrying so fast that he had no choice but to break into a run. He was moving fast now, heading straight for the end of the street. Running pell-mell, he reached the corner. Without warning, he suddenly leaped into the air and with one powerful thrust tried to throw his arms away.

One day while frying some pork chops she melted onto the kitchen floor in the shape of a poached egg.

He walked into a place where many people gather. He had a companion with him. They sat down at a single table that was covered with a cloth. There was a scene hanging on the wall to the right of them. It was a replica of a landscape, a small hill on one side, an empty space and then a large tree at the other end. A large window stood directly behind them.

He sat for some time without speaking and then slowly put one of his arms on the table. The other immediately crossed his legs. He folded his arms in front of him and looked out of the window. The second uncrossed his legs, turned his body halfway to the window and looked out.

The next day three other people came into the same room. A man, a woman and a small girl. They seated themselves around the cloth covered table and immediately began to speak with each other. After a few seconds they fell silent and remained quite still.

Then the man very carefully put one of his arms on the table and the woman crossed her legs. The man folded his arms in front of him and looked out of the window. The woman then uncrossed her legs and turned her body halfway toward the glass. During this time the small girl sat motionless.

He was lying on a rock holding his hand in the air when a bird came into his view and flew through it.

One afternoon he walked up to the object and appeared before himself. At his side stood a small table. Within the object there appeared an exact duplicate of this table. He stood quite still facing the object for some time and then turned his back to it and walked across the room to a large box. He opened the box and drew out a smaller object of the same nature. As he faced it, a duplicate of himself appeared with a table somewhere in the background. He glanced back across the room to the larger object he had just left and saw that his duplicate was also standing there.

With the smaller object still in his hand, he began to walk out of the room. As he walked, his duplicate within the object never left, but the table disappeared from within it the instant he left the room.

Once, after looking into the instrument for some time, he turned his back to it and stood so close that his back touched it. At exactly the same time and as if the thought occurred to each simultaneously, his duplicate in the object turned his back and leaned against him. They stood still for some time back to back when he reached into his upper suit jacket pocket, pulled out thin strips of paper and began to blow on them. After a long pause, he also put his hand into his upper jacket pocket, pulled out some thin strips of paper and began to blow on them.

One day a large crystal fell from the sky and took twenty years to roll across the table.

He duplicated the clothes of a dead man and dressed up in them. He then took two chairs and set them on the corner of a busy downtown street. He brought along the dead man and setting him upright in one of the chairs, took the other one himself.

He and a companion carried a gray object into the middle of a large empty area. They put it down in the center and both began to place one foot in front of the other, walking away from the object until they had measured some 15 feet from the center. Then they stopped. Both stood at exactly the same distance from the object, each being on one side of it. They faced the object and walked around it, still maintaining the same distance from it. Then they both stood perfectly still in a spot across from each other and looked intently at the object. He closed his eyes and suddenly everything around him vanished.

The wind sitting on the pole blew and blew until it blew the pole down.

He had taken a trip that by air travel had put him one day ahead of his friends. When he returned, he sat very still in a chair while his friends ran as fast as they could in one place.

The memory he had of immersing himself in water could no longer remember him.

He moved the window next to the chair and asked the girl to bend down next to the rock while by answering the telephone he had put the last piece into the jigsaw puzzle.

He was walking down the street talking to his friend John about a hypothetical situation.

"I don't recognize him on the street, so I pass him by, but he recognizes me and stops and says, don't you remember when we met at this building?"

And John, unable to recognize him, walked away.

As he felt a need to change the decor of his room, he went around to each piece of furniture and picked time out of it.

Each day after dinner he took his radio and went outside to relax in a chair. From where he sat he could see the road in front of him and a tree at his side.

This day, after sitting down and switching on the radio, he turned to his side and saw nothing. When he looked in front of him there was also nothing. He found in fact, that he was pinned to the chair.

The radio broadcast was soon interrupted by an emergency announcement reporting that without warning the spaces between things had suddenly drifted away, leaving all people and objects trapped in a pocket of their own shape, and that as soon as the people in charge could find a way to get past their own pocket, they would do their best to dig out the rest of the people.

If he stood still he was Jack, if he moved he was Jim.

When he was first seen he was about 4′ 11″ in height, had light colored hair and a high pitched voice.

Five years later he had managed to elongate himself 10 inches, his hair had darkened considerably, and his voice had dropped an octave.

A search was made for the discarded 4′ 11″, light-haired him and he was located living in a room down the hall from the taller one.

He was in his living room with seven stuffed dummies of himself. The first was about to sit in a chair by the window, the second and third were on the divan holding a cup of tea in the air, the fourth in the middle of taking a step, the fifth with his hand reaching for the knob of the door, the sixth and seventh poised over a table game, the eighth holding the record player arm a fraction from the disk, the record beneath spinning round and round.

Each time he appeared with the table, the table appeared with him.

He was sitting in a restaurant talking about the event that had occurred just before he had come in for dinner. He was walking down the street when he noticed that one of the telephone poles along the side of the boulevard had a large indentation in it. When he looked down the block, he saw that the entire line of poles had, at exactly the same place, a whole section of their poles missing.

"Oh," he replied, "I remember seeing the same thing about two years ago on the south side of town."

And he left the restaurant finding two years later as he was walking down a boulevard, a line of poles with a section of themselves removed.

The waitress came up to the table and asked if he was waiting for friends or would he be having his dinner alone.

The mouth decided to join a face that was already here rather than form one of its own.

When he went out to water his garden, he saw that overnight the tomato plants had grown several inches and were ready to eat. He picked a few and taking them into the house, put them on a plate on the table. He cut a section from one of the tomatoes and put it into his mouth. As he bit down and felt the juice spurt around his teeth, he saw on the plate that they were colored pictures clipped from a magazine.

He was running as fast as the tree was standing still.